TEAM 11 PLUS
SET 1
MATHEMATICS PAPERS

Keep track of your performance by filling in the table below

	Percentage	Time Taken	Comments
Test 1			
Test 2			
Test 3			
Test 4			
Test 5			

MATHS

Multiple-choice
Test 1

Read the following carefully.

- o Do not open the booklet until you are instructed to do so.
- o This is a multiple-choice test.
- o Answers should be marked in pencil with a firm line, on the answer sheet, **not** on the test booklet.
- o If you make a mistake, rub it out and write down your new answer.
- o You should only have one answer per question.
- o Choose the answer you think fits best.
- o Do not leave any boxes empty.
- o You will have 25 minutes to do the test.

Author: Ruvini Hewavidana

TEAM 11 PLUS

1

What number completes this equation?

$$200 \div 5 = 33 + \underline{\quad}$$

2

A group of children share a packet of 26 biscuits. They receive 4 biscuits each and there are two biscuits left over.

How many children are in the group?

3

Year 5 did a survey to find out how many people are right-handed and left-handed. They made this pie chart.

If 12 children are left-handed, how many children are right-handed?

4

$$\underline{\quad}, \quad \underline{\quad}, \quad 5, \quad 9, \quad 13, \quad 17$$

What is the first number in the sequence?

5

A £2 coin weighs 12g. Hannah has only £2 coins in her purse. She has £14 in total.

How much do her coins weigh altogether?

6

Dylan spends £8 on a bus ticket and his lunch.
He spends 80p more on his lunch than his bus ticket.

How much did his lunch cost?

TEAM 11 PLUS

7	A bag of sweets weighs 120g. A box can hold 14 bags of sweets. How much does a full box weigh, in kilograms?
8	A new shampoo bottle says it contains 25% extra shampoo. If the old bottle contained 500ml, how much does the new bottle contain?
9	Mr. Sood takes part in a marathon, which is 26 miles long. He runs for half the race, and walks for 5.5 miles. How much further must he go to reach the finish?
10	The shape below is made from three equilateral triangles. What is the value of $3x$?
11	What number completes the second equation? $143 \times 26 = 3718$ $143 \times \ ? \ = 1859$

12	Here are the ages of four children:

Jessica	8 years, 3 months
Callum	7 years, 9 months
Meera	9 years, 1 month
Aidan	8 years, 3 months

What is the mean age of the children, in years and months?

13	Ebun's father weighs 87kg. Ebun weighs two thirds of her father's weight. How much does Ebun weigh, in kilograms?

14

Which of the following shapes has lines of symmetry?

A

B

C

D

E

15

Here are the distances, in kilometres, of various cities from London.

Cairo	3508
Berlin	928
Singapore	10852
Rome	1431
Chicago	6356

What is the difference between the furthest and nearest cities from London?

16

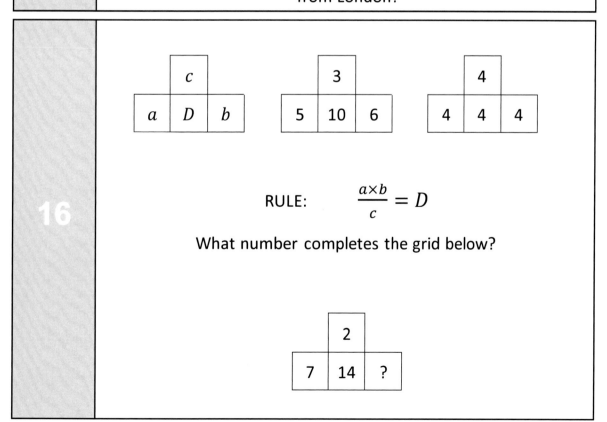

RULE: $\dfrac{a \times b}{c} = D$

What number completes the grid below?

17

The pie chart shows how many people used the different facilities at a sports centre on a particular day.

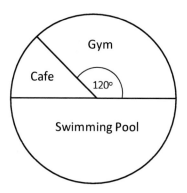

If 86 people used the gym, how many people altogether visited the sports centre on that day?

18

Julien is thinking of a quadrilateral

- It has opposite sides which are parallel.
- All sides are the same length.
- It has only two lines of symmetry.

What shape is Julien thinking of?

19

The bar chart shows the number of children in year 6 who travel to school in different ways.

Which of the following is **incorrect**?
a.) The modal method of travel was by car
b.) 10 more people travelled by bus than by bike
c.) There are 75 children in year 6
d.) 20% of children travel by bus
e.) More than half the children travel by car.

TEAM 11 PLUS

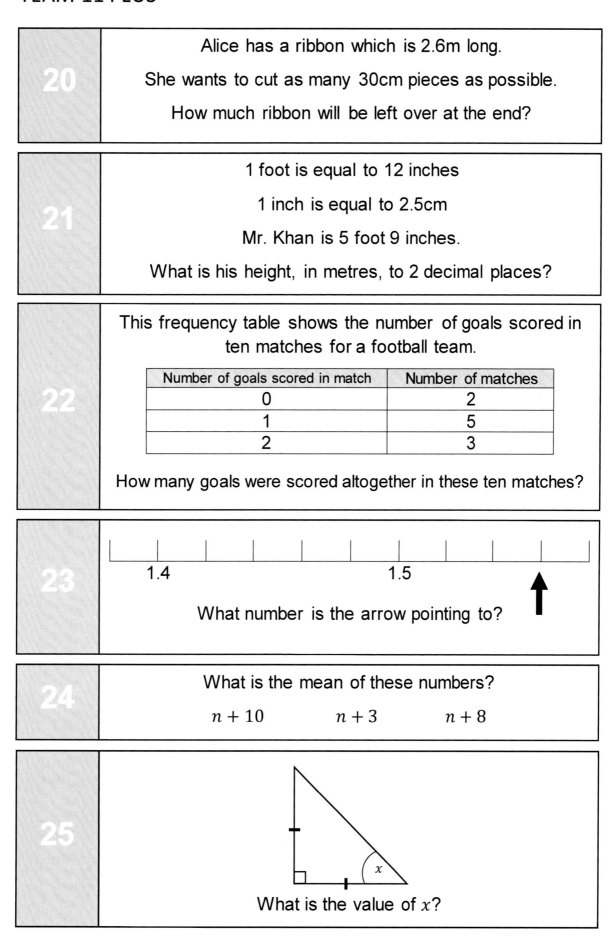

20

Alice has a ribbon which is 2.6m long.

She wants to cut as many 30cm pieces as possible.

How much ribbon will be left over at the end?

21

1 foot is equal to 12 inches

1 inch is equal to 2.5cm

Mr. Khan is 5 foot 9 inches.

What is his height, in metres, to 2 decimal places?

22

This frequency table shows the number of goals scored in ten matches for a football team.

Number of goals scored in match	Number of matches
0	2
1	5
2	3

How many goals were scored altogether in these ten matches?

23

1.4   1.5

What number is the arrow pointing to?

24

What is the mean of these numbers?

$n + 10$ $n + 3$ $n + 8$

25

What is the value of x?

END OF TEST 1

MATHS
Multiple-choice
Test 2

Read the following carefully.

- o Do not open the booklet until you are instructed to do so.
- o This is a multiple-choice test.
- o Answers should be marked in pencil with a firm line, on the answer sheet, **not** on the test booklet.
- o If you make a mistake, rub it out and write down your new answer.
- o You should only have one answer per question.
- o Choose the answer you think fits best.
- o Do not leave any boxes empty.
- o You will have 25 minutes to do the test.

Author: Ruvini Hewavidana

TEAM 11 PLUS

| 1 | Jerome buys 7 cupcakes for £5.95.

How much does each cupcake cost? |

| 2 | Here is a pattern of shapes:

What is the probability of randomly selecting a circle? |

| 3 | What is the value of the 6 in the following number?

46011 |

| 4 | The table shows the distances, in kilometres, between various cities. |

London			
203	**Birmingham**		
50	217	**Guildford**	
99	296	82	**Canterbury**

Mr Nadiwala must travel from Canterbury to London, then from London to Guildford, before finally going back to Canterbury.

How far must he travel altogether, in kilometres?

| 5 | Jasmine signs up for a new mobile contract. |

Calls	Texts	Data
5p per minute	2p per text	£1 per gigabyte

In June, Jasmine made calls for 23 minutes, sent 103 texts and used 1.8 gigabytes of data.

How much will her bill cost this month?

TEAM 11 PLUS

6

Here is a rectangle

The longer sides are four times bigger than the shorter sides.

What is the perimeter of the rectangle?

7

A cube has a volume of 8cm³.

What is the length of each side?

8

What is two million, eighty-one thousand and ten written in figures?

9

Which of the following statements is **incorrect?**

a. The sum of two odd numbers is always an even number.
b. The product of two odd numbers is always an odd number.
c. The product of two even numbers is always even.
d. The product of an odd and even number is always odd
e. The product of an odd and even number is always even.

10

A plant is 3.2m tall. In two weeks, it should be 20% taller.

What height should it be in two weeks?

11

Duncan is stacking boxes. He creates the following pattern:

If Duncan makes five rows, how many boxes will be stacked altogether?

TEAM 11 PLUS

12	A Stagecoach bus leaves Ashford every 5 minutes. An Arriva bus leaves Ashford every 12 minutes. In one hour, how many **more** Stagecoach buses leave Ashford than Arriva buses?

13	What number is 1000 times bigger than 0.228?

14	Michelle and Omar share a pizza. The pizza contains 960 calories. Michelle only eats $\frac{3}{8}$ of the pizza, and Omar eats the rest. How many calories has Omar consumed?

15	At the start of March, Georgia has £1,750 in her bank account. During the month, she spends £823. At the end of the March, she receives her monthly salary of £2,497 How much money is in her account at the start of April?

16	Which of these statements is **incorrect**? a. $-5 < -4$ b. $-1 > -9$ c. $5 > -6$ d. $-9 > -5$ e. $-6 < -2$

17	Candis has a tennis lesson at 12:10. It takes exactly 23 minutes to walk from her house to the tennis lesson. What is the latest time she should leave?

18	Mr. Picknell needs 158 tiles to decorate his bathroom. If tiles come in packs of thirty, how many packs must he buy?

19

Here is a Venn diagram:

In which section would the number 2 go?

20

Jon must take 5ml of medicine, 3 times a day for a week.

The medicine bottle contains 175ml of medicine.

How much medicine will be left in the bottle at the end of the week?

21

What are the coordinates of point Q?

22

Prithan uses some regular hexagons to make a pattern.
Each hexagon has sides of length 5cm.

What is the perimeter of this new shape?

23	$$x^2 - 3$$ What is the value of the expression above when $x = 6$?

24	A postman delivers letters to all the houses on an estate. There are 150 houses altogether. He notices that $\frac{2}{5}$ of the front doors are painted white, and 30% of the front doors are painted brown. The rest are a different colour. Which of the following is **incorrect?** a. 60 houses have white front doors b. There are 15 more white front doors than brown ones c. 45 front doors are a different colour d. 30% of the doors are a different colour e. There modal colour is brown

25	Here are the prices for cinema tickets and various snacks available at CinemaWorld.

	Tickets
Child	£4.50
Adult	£6.50

	Popcorn	Drinks	Sweets
Small	£3	£2.50	£2
Large	£4	£3.50	£4

Mr. and Mrs. Rai take their two children to see a new film.

They will share one small popcorn, two large popcorns, two large drinks, and a large bag of sweets.

How much does it cost them altogether for the tickets, food and drink?

END OF TEST 2

MATHS
Multiple-choice
Test 3

Read the following carefully.

- o Do not open the booklet until you are instructed to do so.
- o This is a multiple-choice test.
- o Answers should be marked in pencil with a firm line, on the answer sheet, **not** on the test booklet.
- o If you make a mistake, rub it out and write down your new answer.
- o You should only have one answer per question.
- o Choose the answer you think fits best.
- o Do not leave any boxes empty.
- o You will have 25 minutes to do the test.

© 2016 Team11Plus

Author: Ruvini Hewavidana

TEAM 11 PLUS

1

What number completes this equation?

_____ + 5.6 = 12 − 2.4

2

Kim goes shopping at the supermarket. Her items should cost £56.90.

She has a coupon, which gives her 10% off her total.

How much will she have to pay at the checkout?

3

Year 7 children choose what language they would like to study when they enter secondary school. The pie chart shows their choices.

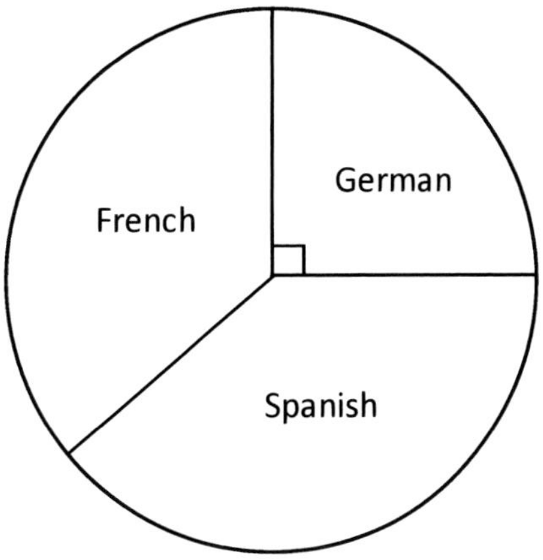

If there were 180 children altogether, how many children chose German?

4

Which of the following shapes has **more than** two lines of symmetry?

a. Rectangle
b. Rhombus
c. Regular hexagon
d. Isosceles triangle
e. Oval

5

What number completes the equation?

_____ x 6 = 84

6

Adowa baked 72 gingerbread men for a bake sale. $\frac{1}{9}$ of them were damaged and thrown away. The rest were sold for 30p each.

How much money did she make from selling the gingerbread men?

7

X is the mid-point of the rectangle ABCD, which is shown below. What are the coordinates of X?

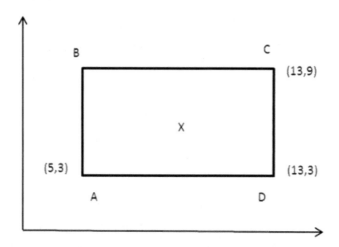

8

Mr. Stevens is going on holidays and takes with him these two suitcases.

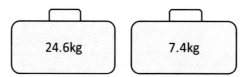

The maximum baggage weight is 35kg.

What is the difference between the weight of his suitcases and the maximum baggage weight?

9

What number completes the equation?

97 x 8 = 776

97 x __ = 1552

TEAM 11 PLUS

10	What is the value of the 5 in the number 805,221?

11	A music performance at a school consists of two halves. Both halves are 35 minutes each. Also, there is a 15-minute break in between the two halves. If the performance starts at 6:00pm, when does it finish?

12 — What is the area of this compound shape?

8m, 4m, 9m, 8m, 4m, 17m

13	Mrs. Smith can type 12 pages in 50 minutes. How long would it take her to type 30 pages?

14 — What is the area of this triangle?

12cm, 6cm

15	Owen goes on holiday for a fortnight starting on 18th March. On what date does he return?

16	What is 319 divided by 5?

17	To make 8 cupcakes, Toluwa needs 180g of flour. How much flour does she need to make 40 cup cakes?

18

$$75 < x < 89$$

x is a square number. What is the value of x?

19

The graph shows the amount of people who bought packets of trading cards in a newsagents one day.

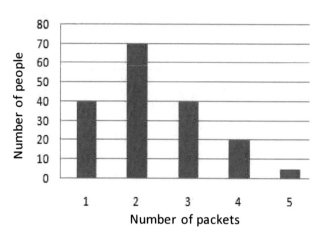

How many packets were bought altogether on that day?

20

Brian's exam results are as follows:

English	64%
French	62%
Science	75%
Maths	67%
History	62%

What is the mean percentage for his exams?

21

Here is a spinner,

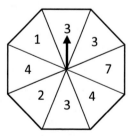

Frankie will spin the spinner 200 times.

How many times should the spinner land on the number 3?

22	What number completes the equation? $$\frac{2}{5} + \underline{\quad} = 1$$

23	At the weekend, Dinum cycles 2.8km. Ryan cycles 1.7km further than Dinum. Katy cycles twice as far as Ryan. How far did Katy cycle at the weekend?

24	Hermali buys 2 apples for x pence each and 4 kiwis for y pence each. Which expression represents the total cost, in pence?

25	The rectangle and square below have the same area.

9cm

4cm

What is the length of one side of the square?

END OF TEST 3

MATHS
Multiple-choice
Test 4

Read the following carefully.

- ○ Do not open the booklet until you are instructed to do so.
- ○ This is a multiple-choice test.
- ○ Answers should be marked in pencil with a firm line, on the answer sheet, **not** on the test booklet.
- ○ If you make a mistake, rub it out and write down your new answer.
- ○ You should only have one answer per question.
- ○ Choose the answer you think fits best.
- ○ Do not leave any boxes empty.
- ○ You will have 25 minutes to do the test.

Author: Ruvini Hewavidana

TEAM 11 PLUS

1

Sanjay jumped the following distances in the long jump.

5.5m	4.9m	5.3m
4.8m	5.3m	5.0m

What is the range of the distances?

2

What is $\frac{1}{4}$ of 3528?

3

Rowan's calculator displays the following number:

13.6749274

His teacher asks him to round it to the nearest tenth.

What number should he write down?

4

Yumna has 2kg of 50p coins.

Each 50p coin weighs 10g.

What is the total value of her coins?

5

In a shop till, there are:

twenty 5p coins, fifteen 10p coins, twelve 50p coins and sixty £1 coins.

How much money is that altogether?

6

Which shape below has rotational symmetry of order 4?

A   B   C

D   E

TEAM 11 PLUS

7	Chris buys a DVD for £12.50. The shop has a sale for 20% off the price of all DVDs. How much does Chris pay after the price reduction?
8	£1 = $1.31 Rachael converts £12 into dollars. How many dollars does she get?
9	Here is a sequence with numbers missing. 8, _____, _____, 26 The gaps between each of the numbers is equal. What numbers are missing?

10

Here are two equal right-angled triangles.

4cm 5cm 3cm

Hugh joins these triangles together to form an isosceles triangle. What is the perimeter of this new shape?

11	What is $\frac{3}{5}$ as a percentage?
12	5 miles is equal to 8km. How many miles are there in 560km?
13	82,748 sports fan watch the Olympics 100m final in the Olympic stadium. What is this number rounded to the nearest thousand?

14

This pie chart shows the number of people who own different electronic devices in a class.

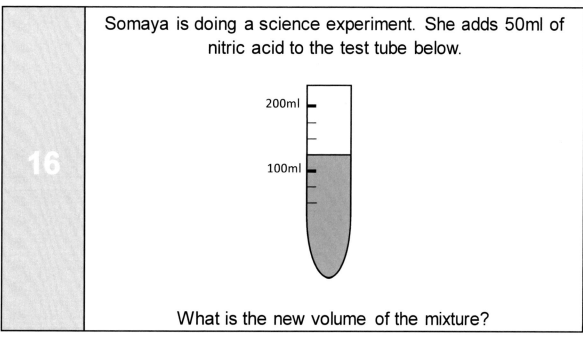

6 people own an iPod. How many people took part in the survey?

15

18cm

7cm

What is the area of the shaded square?

16

Somaya is doing a science experiment. She adds 50ml of nitric acid to the test tube below.

200ml

100ml

What is the new volume of the mixture?

17

Which of these statements is correct?

a. $1\frac{1}{4} = 1.4$

b. $1.25 > 1.4$

c. $1\frac{1}{4} < 1.4$

d. $1.5 < 1.4$

e. $1\frac{1}{2} < 1.4$

18

The angles in a triangle are x, $2x$, and $3x$.

What is the size of the biggest angle?

19

Cynthia thinks of a number.

She squares it and adds 9. Her answer is 130.

What number did she start with?

20

A 4kg bag of potatoes is split into 5 equal portions.

How big is each portion?

21

How many vertices does this octahedron have?

22

Clyde finished in second place in the 100m race with a time of 12.84 seconds. Usain's time was $\frac{1}{4}$ quicker.

What was Usain's winning time?

23	On a map 2cm represents 5km in real life. If the distance between two cities is 12.5km in real life, what is the distance on the map?

24	14 oranges cost £2.10. 5 plums cost £1.40. What is the difference between the cost of an orange and the cost of a plum?

25	The size of a popcorn packet and a serving tray are shown below. 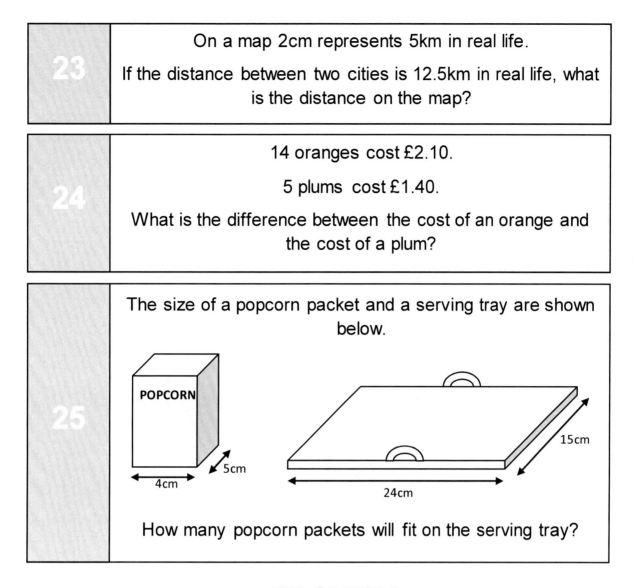 How many popcorn packets will fit on the serving tray?

END OF TEST 4

MATHS
Multiple-choice
Test 5

Read the following carefully.

- ○ Do not open the booklet until you are instructed to do so.
- ○ This is a multiple-choice test.
- ○ Answers should be marked in pencil with a firm line, on the answer sheet, **not** on the test booklet.
- ○ If you make a mistake, rub it out and write down your new answer.
- ○ You should only have one answer per question.
- ○ Choose the answer you think fits best.
- ○ Do not leave any boxes empty.
- ○ You will have 25 minutes to do the test.

Author: Ruvini Hewavidana

TEAM 11 PLUS

1

What weight is the arrow pointing to below?

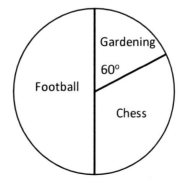

2

Subaz thinks of a number. He divides it by three and adds twenty. The answer is 153.

What number did he start with?

3

The table below shows the favourite drinks of 35 children.

	Fizzy Drinks	Fruit Juice	Other
Boys	9	5	3
Girls	?	9	4

How many girls liked fizzy drinks best?

4

What number completes the equation?

2023 - _____ = 747

5

Arya saves up thirteen £1 coins, sixty-five 50p coins, eight 20p coins and five 2p coins.

How much money does Arya have?

6

The pie chart shows the number of people who take part in various after-school clubs.

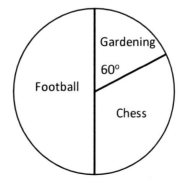

17 children go to gardening club. How many go to football club?

TEAM 11 PLUS

7	A TV show starts at quarter to 3 in the afternoon. It lasts 35 minutes. At what time will it end?
8	$\frac{1}{20}$ of a T-shirt is made of polyester. What percentage is this?
9	Dinil wants to make pancakes. He has 0.132kg of flour. His recipe needs 400g of flour. How much more flour does he need to buy?

10

The table below shows the number of people who shop on different days of the week.

Monday	15
Tuesday	7
Wednesday	8
Thursday	17
Friday	28
Saturday	74
Sunday	67

What is the modal shopping day?

11	560 people visit a garden centre on Saturday. One fifth of them buy a sunflower for £2.60 each. How much money does the garden centre make from selling sunflowers on Saturday?
12	What number on the answer sheet is the smallest?
13	Hiring a bike costs £10 **plus** an additional £5 per hour. Betty hires a bike for x hours. What is the total cost in pounds?

TEAM 11 PLUS

14	What is $\frac{17}{20}$ as a percentage?

15	Dinaadi has a sore throat. She must take 5ml of medicine three times each day. The medicine bottle holds 0.18L of medicine. How many days will the bottle last?

16	On a map, the scale is 2cm = 1km If the distance between two towns is 2.5km in real life, how far apart would they be on the map?

17	A (2,8) C B (16,1) What are the coordinates of point C?

18	Below is an equilateral triangle. x^o What is the value of x?

19	Below are the instructions to work out the cooking time for a leg of lamb. *Cook for 35mins, plus an additional 40mins per kilogram.* Olivia is cooking a 3.5kg leg of lamb How long will it take her to cook, in hours and minutes?

TEAM 11 PLUS

20	Charlie has the following cards: $\boxed{6}$ $\boxed{7}$ $\boxed{9}$ $\boxed{5}$ $\boxed{8}$ $\boxed{3}$ What is the largest **even** number he can make, using all six of the cards at once?
21	The pre-tax cost of a plane ticket to Italy is £96. Musnum must pay tax, which is 20% of the ticket's cost. How much will the ticket cost after tax?

22

The price of zoo tickets is shown below:

Adult	£10.50
Child	£4.50
Family (2 adults, 2 children)	£25.00

Mr. O'Connor treats his wife and two children to a day out at the zoo.

How much money do they save by paying for the family ticket, rather than 4 individual tickets?

23

The scatter graph below shows the temperature at different times during the day in Madrid.

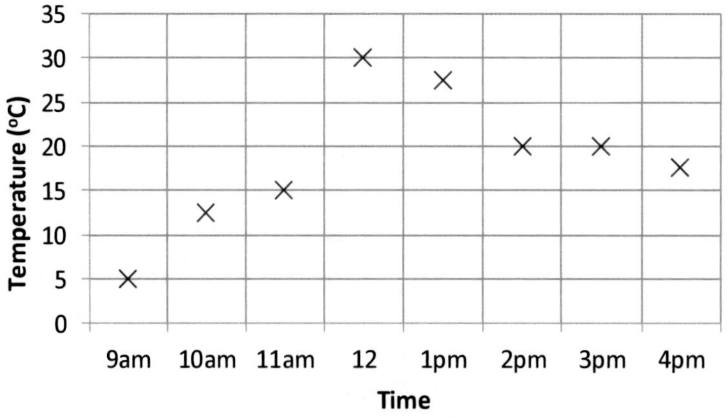

What is the range of temperatures?

24

The compound shape below shows a square attached to two equilateral triangles.

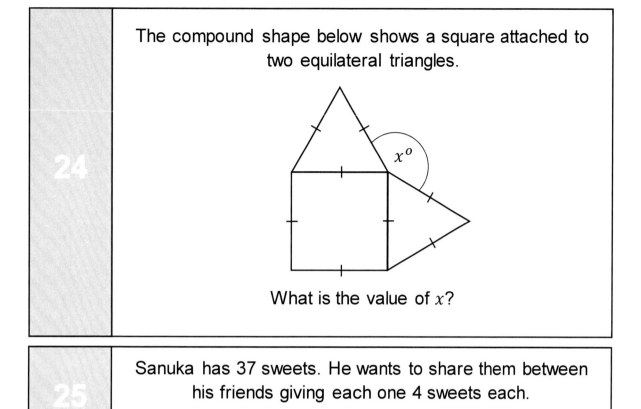

What is the value of x?

25

Sanuka has 37 sweets. He wants to share them between his friends giving each one 4 sweets each.

How many friends can he share his sweets with?

END OF TEST 5